ADVENTURE TIME ™

THE FOUR CASTLES

ADVENTURE TIME: THE FOUR CASTLES
ISBN - 978-1-78585-2-916

Published by Titan Comics, a division of Titan Publishing Group Ltd., 144 Southwark St., London, SE1 0UP. ADVENTURE TIME,
CARTOON NETWORK, the logos, and all related characters and elements are trademarks of and © Cartoon Network. (S16) All rights
reserved. All characters, events and institutions depicted herein are fictional. Any similarity between any of the names, characters,
persons, events and/or institutions in this publication to actual names, characters, and persons, whether living or dead and/or
institutions are unintended and purely coincidental. TCN 1647

A CIP catalogue record for this title is available from the British Library.

Printed in China.

10 9 8 7 6 5 4 3 2 1

Created by Pendleton Ward

Written by **Josh Trujillo**

Illustrated by **Zachary Sterling & Phil Murphy**

Inks by **Phil Murphy**

Colours by **Kat Efird**

Letters by **Warren Montgomery**

Cover by **Scott Maynard**

With Special Thanks to Marisa Marionakis, Rick Blanco, Curtis Lelash, Conrad Montgomery, Meghan Bradley, Kelly Crews, Scott Malchus, Adam Muto and the wonderful folks at Cartoon Network.

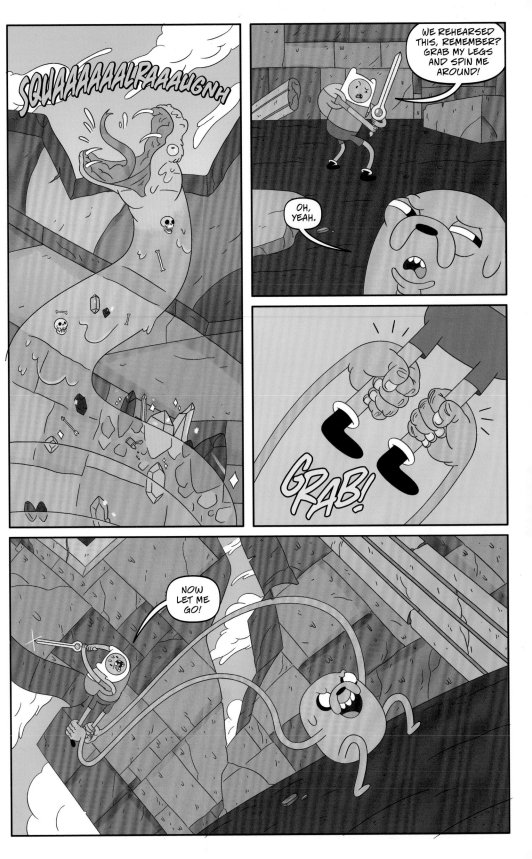

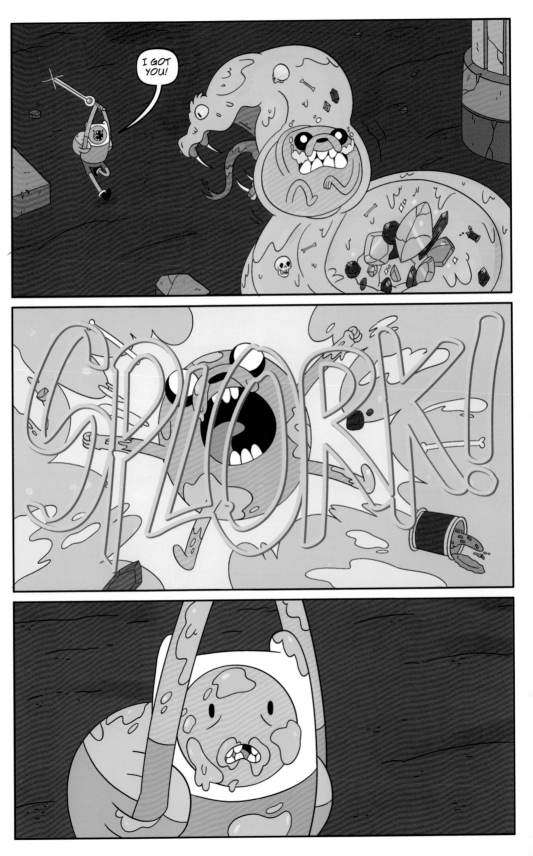

THE EVERCOMB

The envy of all combs everywhere, The Evercomb is the finest grooming tool in the Land of Ooo. Tradition dictates that only the fairest maidens shall wield its' beauteous luster.

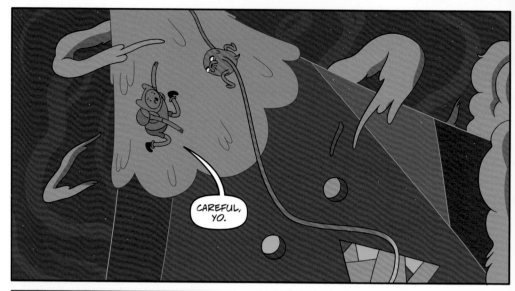

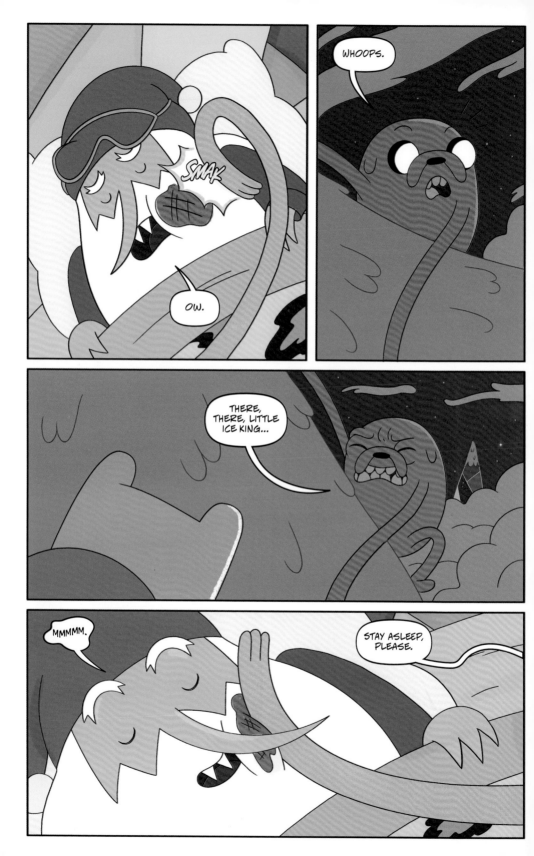

WHOEVER YOU ARE, YOU'RE IN BIG TROUBLE!

ARRRRAAAAAAA!

POOF

HA HA

HA

PHANTASMAL LOOKING GLASS

POLTERGEISTS AND VAMPIRES ARE ABLE TO SEE THEIR MAGICALLY PERFECT REFLECTION IN ITS SILVERY SURFACE. IT WAS A FAVORITE OF THE HAUNTED ELITE UNTIL THEY LEARNED THAT TRUE BEAUTY COMES FROM BATHING IN THE BLOOD OF INNOCENTS.

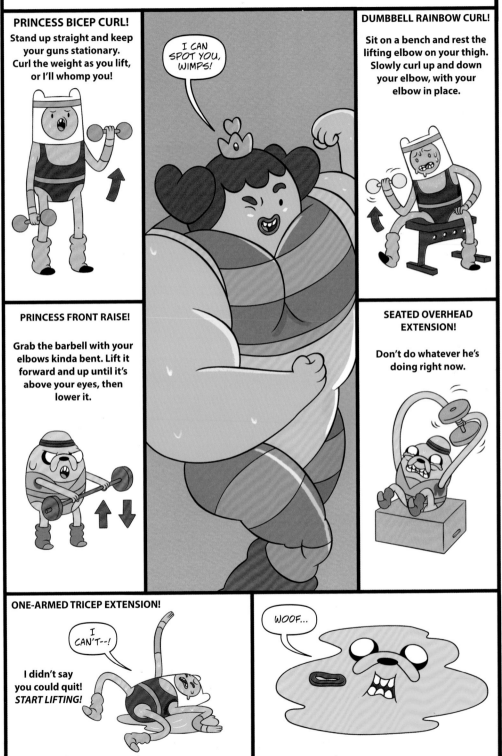

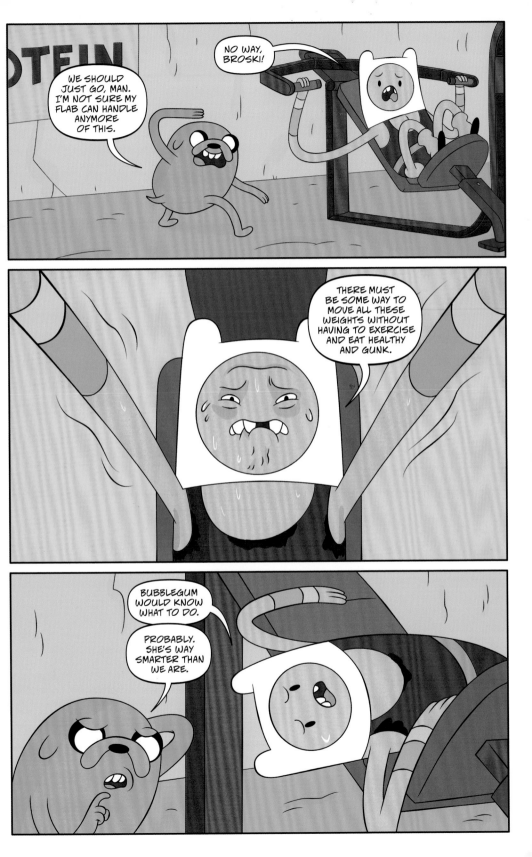

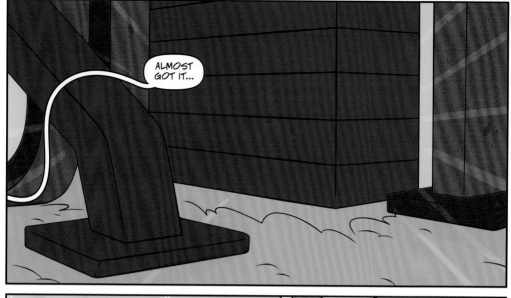

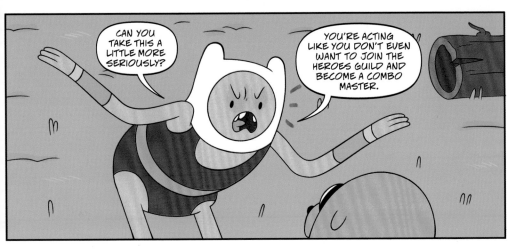

HOUR NUMBER FOUR.

I, BMO, HAVE BEEN TRAPPED BY THE VILLAINOUS GUILDMASTER.

MY BEST FRIENDS FINN AND JAKE HAVE BEEN HOODWINKED AND ARE CARRYING OUT A DASTARDLY AND DANGEROUS MISSION.

MY ENERGY RESERVES HAVE TURNED COLD.

WITH RESCUE UNLIKELY, I MUST ENTER SLEEP MODE AND DREAM OF FREEDOM...

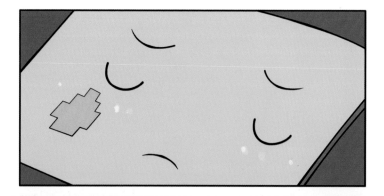

THE RIGHT EARRING OF WACOOMB

Lost to history, or perhaps a stray cat or something, the Right Earring of Wacoomb is a legendary fashion accessory. Those brave enough to unite the pair risk destroying sensibilities everywhere.

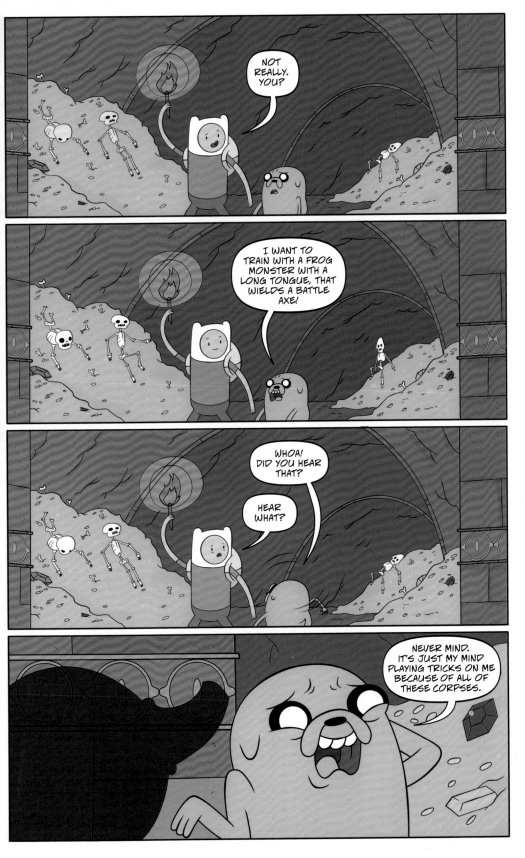

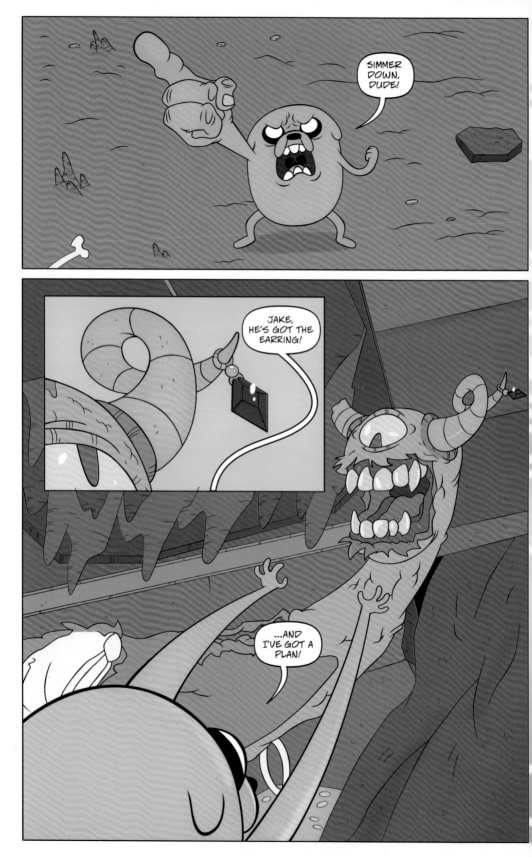

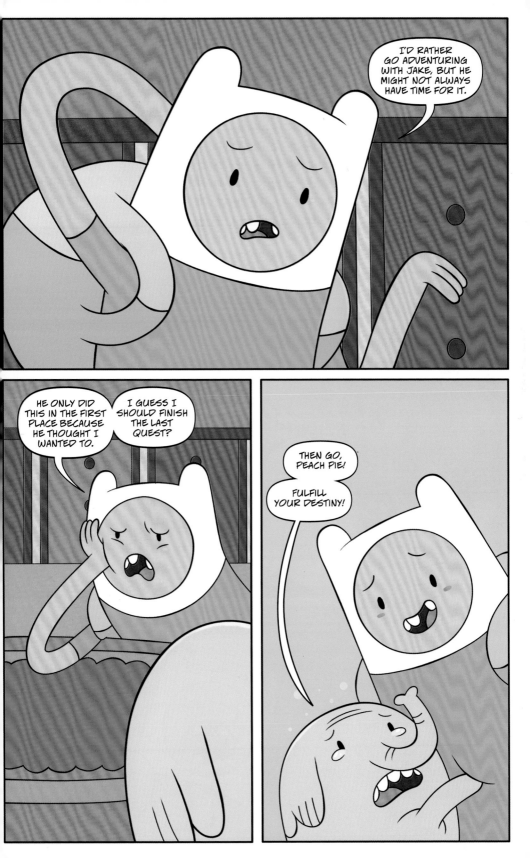

THE BRACERS OF BROMAGE

It is said the fate of the universe is vested in these two silver bracers. They are also great for casual wear and match almost anything.

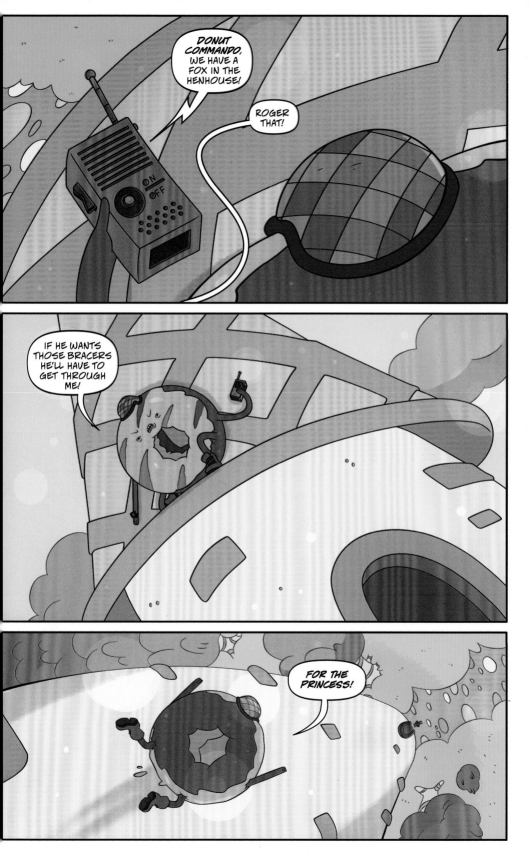

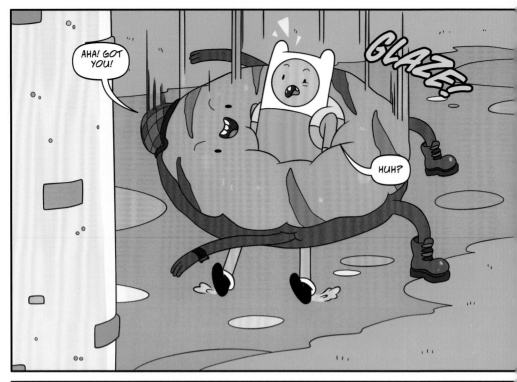

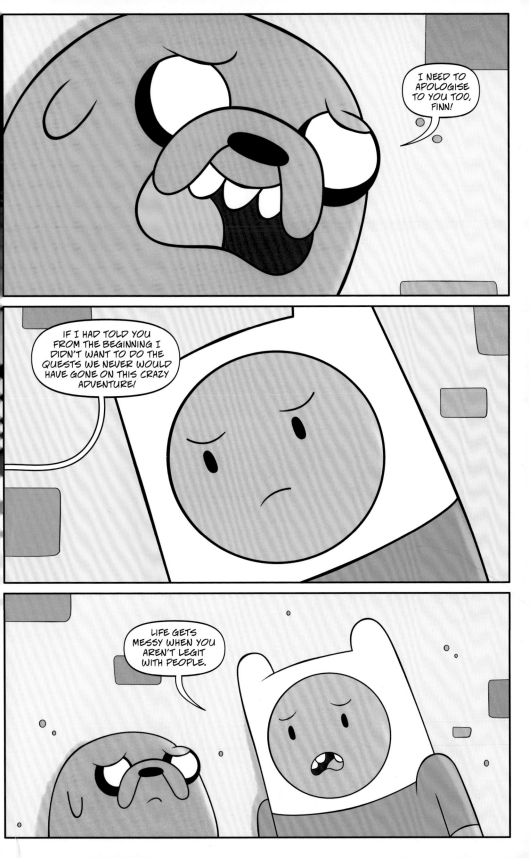